Ready? Set! Go!

Congratulations! You made the team!

You have been chosen for the great Which Way USA race across America! All you need to pack is your imagination, sense of humor, and brainpower. Along with your teammates, Tripp Wilson and Scout Sanchez, you will explore each of the fifty United States, solving puzzles and collecting facts as you go.

Sound like fun? It is, but watch out! You're competing against eighteen wacky teams who want to win, too. That's why Tripp and Scout need your help. Every puzzle YOU solve earns bonus points for your team.

Each new Which Way USA race will arrive in the mail. You'll receive a puzzle book and a map for two states. You'll get a bonus, too: a collectible license plate tag for each state.

Sounds great, right? So what are you waiting for?

W9-AZQ-523

Official Game Guide

Keep this Official **Which Way USA** Game Guide handy at all times. Use it to keep track of your progress as you race from state to state.

State-by-State Tracker

PLAYER PROFILE:

_____
(print your name here)

Age: _____ Home state: _____

Can't live without my: _____

_____

Skills and talents I'm proud of:_____

_____

_____

My favorite puzzles to solve:_____

_____

What I hope to see, learn, and do:_____

_____

_____

(paste your picture here)

PLAYER PROFILE: # Tripp Wilson

Age: _____12_____

Can't live without my: ___Tablet computer.___

How else will we get the info we need to know to win the race?

Skills and talents I'm proud of: ___I am an awesome skateboarder. And I'm really good when it comes to taking care of animals—including penguins!___

What I hope to see, learn, and do: ___

• _Ride as many roller coasters as possible_

• _Stand on top of the tallest building in America_

• _See a 10-foot-tall roadrunner!?!_

PLAYER PROFILE: Scout Sanchez

Age: _____12_____

Can't live without my: _____Backpack. If we run_____

_____into a problem during the race, I bet I can turn_____

_____some of the stuff in it into the perfect solution._____

Skills and talents I'm proud of: _____I love the outdoors_____

_____and can walk, hike, trot, jog, climb, scramble, and_____

_____ramble along any trail!_____

What I hope to see, learn, and do: _____

• Ride a surfboard in the Pacific Ocean

• Train to be an astronaut

• Learn to twirl a lasso like a real cowpoke

5

Also in the Running

Tripp, Scout, and you will face off against three pairs of challengers in every state.

May the best team win!

Aretha Flowers and Beau Kay: florists

Boris and Ivana Wynn: former Olympic ice skaters

Bubba Gum and Pops: candy store owner and his grandson

Hyde and Zeke: detective and his assistant

Kareem Cheese and Shelly: sandwich shop owners

Kent Stop and Stu Late: city bus drivers

Laverne and Burly: personal trainers

Mel Box and Fred Ex: mail carriers

Charley and Rhoda Horse: ranchers

Clueless and Lark: off-course explorers

Eb and Flo: plumbers

Flora and Fawn: biologist and her daughter

Huck Hyuck and Lotta Laughs: standup comedians

Penn and Speller: spelling-bee champ and her coach

Rabbit and Cadabra: magician and his assistant

Ruff and Rocky Rhodes: motocross champions

Topsy and Turvy: circus acrobats

Zig and Zag: brother and sister skateboarders

Game Rules

Along with Tripp and Scout, you will compete against three teams in each state.

Your team will visit twelve famous places in each state. At each one, Tripp and Scout must complete a challenge. They might have to dash to the top of a skyscraper, find a rare zoo animal, or win a lawn-mower race!

You also have a challenge—to solve a brainteaser or puzzle of some kind. Some puzzles require that you use your state map. Remember: for every puzzle you solve, your team earns bonus points!

Keep an eye out for other competitors! They are usually around somewhere.

...nds of peppers are hidden in ...y one way. Use the number ...t might fit. Fill them all in ...Way Kids on page 29.

Look for the yellow boxes!
They will tell you how to collect bonus points for your team.

Remember: for every puzzle you solve, our team earns bonus points!

In Control

The next stop is the Johnson Space Center in Houston. Tripp and Scout go straight to the Mission Control Center, where scientists direct astronauts when they are in outer space. Right now, the Which Way kids have a job to do – they must successfully act as Mission Control for a simulated landing on Mars!

"Let's take this race into space!" says Scout, grabbing her headset.

YOU can help Tripp and Scout. Study these two pictures. Can you find at least 20 differences? If you do, give yourself 10 points on page 29.

22

Answer on page 31 23

9

State Puzzle Books

Every state adventure begins the same way: **Ready? Set! Go!**

After Tripp, Scout, and you meet your opponents, the race is on! You can follow the action in order or jump around to your favorite puzzles. Whatever you do, be sure to solve as many puzzles as you can. The more puzzles you solve, the more bonus points you earn for your team.

As you solve puzzles, keep track of your points on page 29.

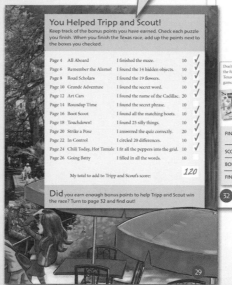

You Helped Tripp and Scout!
Keep track of the bonus points you have earned. Check each puzzle you finish. When you finish the Texas race, add up the points next to the boxes you checked.

Page 4	All Aboard	I finished the maze.	10	✓
Page 6	Remember the Alamo!	I found the 14 hidden objects.	10	✓
Page 8	Road Scholars	I found the 19 flowers.	10	✓
Page 10	Grande Adventure	I found the secret word.	10	✓
Page 12	Art Cars	I found the name of the Cadillac.	20	✓
Page 14	Roundup Time	I found the secret phrase.	10	
Page 16	Boot Scoot	I found all the matching boots.	10	✓
Page 18	Touchdown!	I found 25 silly things.	10	✓
Page 20	Strike a Pose	I answered the quiz correctly.	10	✓
Page 22	In Control	I circled 20 differences.	10	✓
Page 24	Chili Today, Hot Tamale	I fit all the peppers into the grid.	10	✓
Page 26	Going Batty	I filled in all the words.	10	

My total to add to Tripp and Scout's score: **120**

Did you earn enough bonus points to help Tripp and Scout win the race? Turn to page 32 and find out!

29

Turn to page 32 and find out!

And the Winner Is ...

Tripp and Scout earned 150 points for finishing third. Write your bonus points in the box and add it to their total. Did they win the race?

Want to get some Texas barbecue before we leave?

You read my mind!

Don't forget to write the final results on the Texas page of your game guide.

WHICH WAY USA

FINISHERS	Charley and Rhoda Horse	Topsy and Turvy	Tripp and Scout	Kent Stop and Stu Late
SCORE	200	175	150	125
BONUS POINTS	60	90	*120*	100
FINAL TOTAL	*260*	*265*	*270*	*225*

32

Add your bonus points to see if your team has enough to win the race.

When you complete each race, enter your point total and the winning team's name on the state page in this game guide. Attach the stickers from the center of the puzzle book, too!

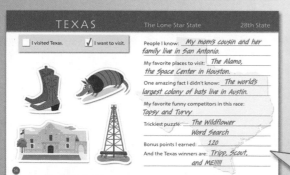

TEXAS
The Lone Star State   28th State

☐ I visited Texas.   ✓ I want to visit.

People I know: *My mom's cousin and her family live in San Antonio.*

My favorite places to visit: *The Alamo, the Space Center in Houston.*

One amazing fact I didn't know: *The world's largest colony of bats live in Austin.*

My favorite funny competitors in this race: *Topsy and Turvy*

Trickiest puzzle: *The Wildflower Word Search*

Bonus points I earned: *120*

And the Texas winners are: *Tripp, Scout, and ME!!!!!*

10

State Maps

You will find helpful information and fun facts on the front of each state map. Use your map to solve two of the puzzles in each book.

The back of the map has awesome photos, descriptions, and messages from Tripp and Scout. See if you agree with what they say.

Highlights WHICH WAY USA

TEXAS

SIX FLAGS A-FLYING
Six flags fly over the State Capitol because Texas has been part of six different nations: Spain, France, Mexico, the Republic of Texas, the Confederate States of America, and the United States of America.

DON'T RATTLE ME!
More than one hundred kinds of snakes slither around in Texas, including 15 poisonous species.

ONE HUGE STATE
Texas is as big as all of New England plus the states of Illinois, New York, Ohio, and Pennsylvania combined!

YEE-HAW!
Modern-day cowboys flock to the Houston Livestock Show and Rodeo—the largest rodeo.

NOT BAAA-D
Texas produces more wool than any other state—nearly 4 million pounds a year!

THEY'VE GOT THE BEAT!
Austin, Texas, is known as the live music capital of the world. Every year, it hosts the South by Southwest music festival, one of the largest music festivals in the country.

TEXAS FACT PACK

STATE SYMBOLS

Flower	Bluebonnet
Bird	Mockingbird
Tree	Pecan
Insect	Monarch Butterfly
Plant	Prickly pear cactus
Reptile	Texas horned lizard
Dish	Chili
Gem	Texas blue topaz

FACTS

Capital	Austin
Population*	25,145,561
Nickname	The Lone Star State
Motto	Friendship
State Song	"Texas, Our Texas"
Visitor's Guide	www.traveltex.com

GEOGRAPHY

Area: 261,231 square miles
Size Rank: 2nd largest
Borders: Louisiana, Arkansas, Oklahoma, New Mexico, Mexico, Gulf of Mexico
Highest Point: Guadalupe Peak, 8,749 feet
Lowest Point: Sea level
Major Rivers: Rio Grande, Red, Brazos
Mountain Ranges: Guadalupe, Davis, Chisos

HISTORY

1528	Spaniard Alvar Núñez Cabeza de Vaca and three others are shipwrecked on Galveston Island and spend the next eight years wandering across Texas.
1718	Spaniards build a fort and a mission near what is now San Antonio.
1821	Mexico declares independence from Spain and claims ownership of Texas.
1836	The Republic of Texas wins its independence from Mexico.
1845	On December 29, Texas becomes the 28th state in the U.S.
1900	One of the worst hurricanes in history rips through Galveston.
1901	The Lucas Gusher at Spindletop Oil Field begins the Texas oil boom.
1963	President John F. Kennedy is assassinated in Dallas. Lyndon B. Johnson is sworn in as the 36th president of the United States.
2000	Texas governor George W. Bush is elected the 43rd president of the United States.

Big Bend National

Scout: I agree. But I'm still glad I didn't pose on trip of this rock like you wanted.

Tripp: It would have made a perfect shot!

Scout: I get dizzy just thinking about it!

Tripp: Totally. It's one of the rarest birds in North America!

Scout: And one of the tallest? Remember this one was almost 5 feet tall?

Tripp: Yeah, I think it liked seeing eye-to-eye with you.

Space Center in Houston was

☐ I visited Alabama.   ☐ I want to visit.

People I know: _____

_____

My favorite places to visit: _____

_____

One amazing fact I didn't know: _____

_____

My favorite funny competitors in this race:

_____

Trickiest puzzle: _____

_____

Bonus points I earned: _____

And the Alabama winners are:

_____

12

I visited Alaska.   I want to visit.

People I know: _____

_____

My favorite places to visit: _____

_____

One amazing fact I didn't know: _____

_____

My favorite funny competitors in this race:

_____

Trickiest puzzle: _____

_____

Bonus points I earned: _____

And the Alaska winners are:

_____

☐ I visited Arizona.   ☐ I want to visit.

People I know: _____

_____

My favorite places to visit: _____

_____

One amazing fact I didn't know: _____

_____

My favorite funny competitors in this race:

_____

Trickiest puzzle: _____

_____

Bonus points I earned: _____

And the Arizona winners are:

_____

☐ I visited Arkansas.   ☐ I want to visit.

People I know: _____

_____

My favorite places to visit: _____

_____

One amazing fact I didn't know: _____

_____

My favorite funny competitors in this race:

_____

Trickiest puzzle: _____

_____

Bonus points I earned: _____

And the Arkansas winners are:

_____

☐ I visited California. ☐ I want to visit.

People I know: _____

_____

My favorite places to visit: _____

_____

One amazing fact I didn't know: _____

_____

My favorite funny competitors in this race:

_____

Trickiest puzzle: _____

_____

Bonus points I earned: _____

And the California winners are:

_____

COLORADO

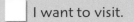 The Centennial State   38th State

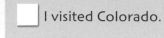 I visited Colorado.   ☐ I want to visit.

People I know: _____

_____

My favorite places to visit: _____

_____

One amazing fact I didn't know: _____

_____

My favorite funny competitors in this race: ____

_____

Trickiest puzzle: _____

_____

Bonus points I earned: _____

And the Colorado winners are:

_____

17

☐ I visited Connecticut.   ☐ I want to visit.

People I know: _____

_____

My favorite places to visit: _____

_____

One amazing fact I didn't know: _____

_____

My favorite funny competitors in this race: _____

_____

Trickiest puzzle: _____

_____

Bonus points I earned: _____

And the Connecticut winners are:

_____

I visited Delaware.   ☐ I want to visit.

People I know: _____

_____

My favorite places to visit: ___ _____

_____

One amazing fact I didn't know: _____

_____

My favorite funny competitors in this race:

_____

Trickiest puzzle: _____

_____

Bonus points I earned: _____

And the Delaware winners are:

_____

19

I visited Florida.

I want to visit.

People I know: _____

_____

My favorite places to visit: _____

_____

One amazing fact I didn't know: _____

_____

My favorite funny competitors in this race:

_____

Trickiest puzzle: _____

_____

Bonus points I earned: _____

And the Florida winners are:

_____

☐ I visited Georgia.   ☐ I want to visit.

People I know: _____

_____

My favorite places to visit: _____

_____

One amazing fact I didn't know: _____

_____

My favorite funny competitors in this race:

_____

Trickiest puzzle: _____

_____

Bonus points I earned: _____

And the Georgia winners are:

_____

21

☐ I visited Hawaii.   ☐ I want to visit.

People I know: _____

_____

My favorite places to visit: _____

_____

One amazing fact I didn't know: _____

_____

My favorite funny competitors in this race:

_____

Trickiest puzzle: _____

_____

Bonus points I earned: _____

And the Hawaii winners are:

_____

I visited Idaho. ☐   I want to visit. ☐

People I know: _____

_____

My favorite places to visit: _____

_____

One amazing fact I didn't know: _____

_____

My favorite funny competitors in this race:

_____

Trickiest puzzle: _____

_____

Bonus points I earned: _____

And the Idaho winners are:

_____

23

I visited Illinois.

I want to visit.

People I know: _____

_____

My favorite places to visit: _____

_____

One amazing fact I didn't know: _____

_____

My favorite funny competitors in this race:

_____

Trickiest puzzle: _____

_____

Bonus points I earned: _____

And the Illinois winners are:

_____

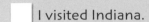 I visited Indiana.   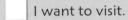 I want to visit.

People I know: _____

_____

My favorite places to visit: _____

_____

One amazing fact I didn't know: _____

_____

My favorite funny competitors in this race:

_____

Trickiest puzzle: _____

_____

Bonus points I earned: _____

And the Indiana winners are:

_____

 I visited Iowa.   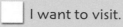 I want to visit.

People I know: _____

_____

My favorite places to visit: _____

_____

One amazing fact I didn't know: _____

_____

My favorite funny competitors in this race:

_____

Trickiest puzzle: _____

_____

Bonus points I earned: _____

And the Iowa winners are:

_____

KANSAS

I visited Kansas.   I want to visit.

People I know: _____

_____

My favorite places to visit: _____ _____

_____

One amazing fact I didn't know: _____

_____

My favorite funny competitors in this race:

_____

Trickiest puzzle: _____

_____

Bonus points I earned: _____

And the Kansas winners are:

_____

☐ I visited Kentucky. ☐ I want to visit.

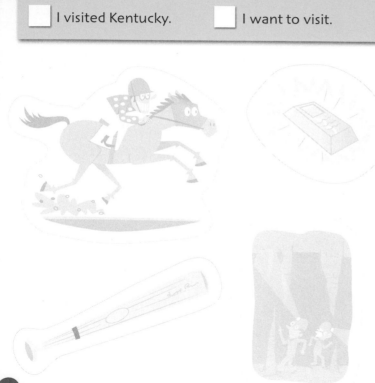

People I know: _____

_____

My favorite places to visit: _____

_____

One amazing fact I didn't know: _____

_____

My favorite funny competitors in this race:

_____

Trickiest puzzle: _____

_____

Bonus points I earned: _____

And the Kentucky winners are:

_____

I visited Louisiana.   I want to visit.

People I know: _____

_____

My favorite places to visit: _____

_____

One amazing fact I didn't know: _____

_____

My favorite funny competitors in this race:

_____

Trickiest puzzle: _____

_____

Bonus points I earned: _____

And the Louisiana winners are:

_____

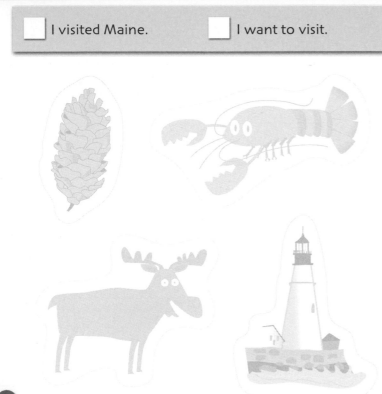

☐ I visited Maine.   ☐ I want to visit.

People I know: _____

_____

My favorite places to visit: _____

_____

One amazing fact I didn't know: _____

_____

My favorite funny competitors in this race:

_____

Trickiest puzzle: _____

_____

Bonus points I earned: _____

And the Maine winners are:

_____

MARYLAND

The Old Line State   7th State

☐ I visited Maryland.   ☐ I want to visit.

People I know: _____

_____

My favorite places to visit: _____

_____

One amazing fact I didn't know: _____

_____

My favorite funny competitors in this race:

_____

Trickiest puzzle: _____

_____

Bonus points I earned: _____

And the Maryland winners are:

_____

☐ I visited Massachusetts. ☐ I want to visit.

People I know: _____

_____

My favorite places to visit: _____

_____

One amazing fact I didn't know: _____

_____

My favorite funny competitors in this race:

_____

Trickiest puzzle: _____

_____

Bonus points I earned: _____

And the Massachusetts winners are:

_____

MICHIGAN

☐ I visited Michigan.   ☐ I want to visit.

People I know: _____

_____

My favorite places to visit: _____

_____

One amazing fact I didn't know: _____

_____

My favorite funny competitors in this race:

_____

Trickiest puzzle: _____

_____

Bonus points I earned: _____

And the Michigan winners are:

_____

☐ I visited Minnesota.   ☐ I want to visit.

People I know: _____

_____

My favorite places to visit: _____

_____

One amazing fact I didn't know: _____

_____

My favorite funny competitors in this race:

_____

Trickiest puzzle: _____

_____

Bonus points I earned: _____

And the Minnesota winners are:

_____

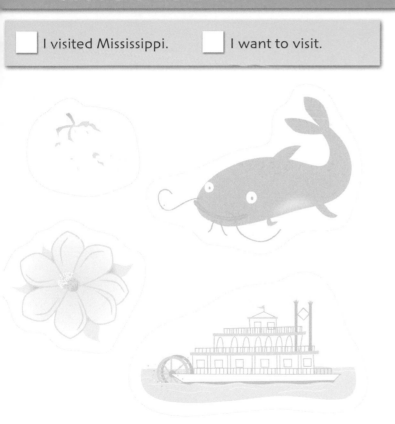

☐ I visited Mississippi.   ☐ I want to visit.

People I know: _____
_____

My favorite places to visit: _____
_____

One amazing fact I didn't know: _____
_____

My favorite funny competitors in this race:
_____

Trickiest puzzle: _____
_____

Bonus points I earned: _____
And the Mississippi winners are:
_____

☐ I visited Missouri.   ☐ I want to visit.

People I know: _____

_____

My favorite places to visit: _____

_____

One amazing fact I didn't know: _____

_____

My favorite funny competitors in this race:

_____

Trickiest puzzle: _____

_____

Bonus points I earned: _____

And the Missouri winners are:

_____

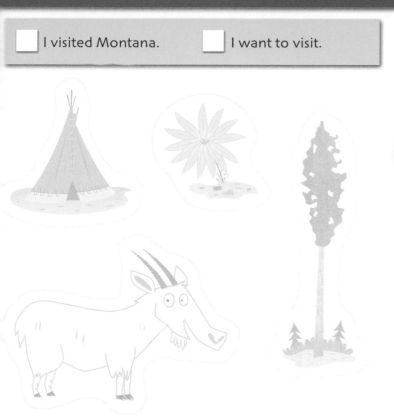

☐ I visited Montana.   ☐ I want to visit.

People I know: _____

_____

My favorite places to visit: _____

_____

One amazing fact I didn't know: _____

_____

My favorite funny competitors in this race:

_____

Trickiest puzzle: _____

_____

Bonus points I earned: _____

And the Montana winners are:

_____

☐ I visited Nebraska.   ☐ I want to visit.

People I know: _____

_____

My favorite places to visit: _____

_____

One amazing fact I didn't know: _____

_____

My favorite funny competitors in this race: _____

_____

Trickiest puzzle: _____

_____

Bonus points I earned: _____

And the Nebraska winners are:

_____

NEVADA

I visited Nevada.   I want to visit.

People I know: _____

_____

My favorite places to visit: _____

_____

One amazing fact I didn't know: _____

_____

My favorite funny competitors in this race:

_____

Trickiest puzzle: _____

_____

Bonus points I earned: _____

And the Nevada winners are:

_____

I visited New Hampshire. ☐ I want to visit.

People I know: _____

_____

My favorite places to visit: _____

_____

One amazing fact I didn't know: _____

_____

My favorite funny competitors in this race:

_____

Trickiest puzzle: _____

_____

Bonus points I earned: _____

And the New Hampshire winners are:

_____

40

I visited New Jersey.　☐　I want to visit.

People I know: _____

_____

My favorite places to visit: _____

_____

One amazing fact I didn't know: _____

_____

My favorite funny competitors in this race:

_____

Trickiest puzzle: _____

_____

Bonus points I earned: _____

And the New Jersey winners are:

_____

☐ I visited New Mexico.   ☐ I want to visit.

People I know: _____

_____

My favorite places to visit: _____

_____

One amazing fact I didn't know: _____

_____

My favorite funny competitors in this race: _____

_____

Trickiest puzzle: _____

_____

Bonus points I earned: _____

And the New Mexico winners are:

_____

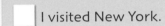 I visited New York.   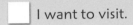 I want to visit.

People I know: _____

_____

My favorite places to visit: _____

_____

One amazing fact I didn't know: _____

_____

My favorite funny competitors in this race:

_____

Trickiest puzzle: _____

_____

Bonus points I earned: _____

And the New York winners are:

_____

I visited North Carolina.   I want to visit.

People I know: _____

_____

My favorite places to visit: _____

_____

One amazing fact I didn't know: _____

_____

My favorite funny competitors in this race:

_____

Trickiest puzzle: _____

_____

Bonus points I earned: _____

And the North Carolina winners are:

_____

☐ I visited North Dakota.   ☐ I want to visit.

People I know: _____

_____

My favorite places to visit: _____

_____

One amazing fact I didn't know: _____

_____

My favorite funny competitors in this race:

_____

Trickiest puzzle: _____

_____

Bonus points I earned: _____

And the North Dakota winners are:

_____

I visited Ohio.   I want to visit.

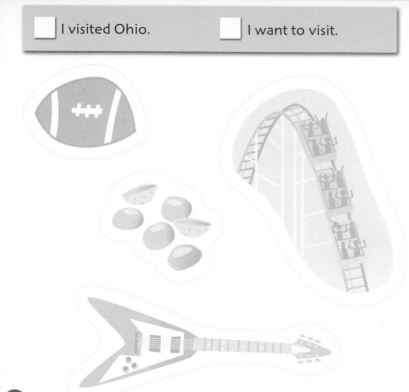

People I know: _____

_____

My favorite places to visit: _____

_____

One amazing fact I didn't know: _____

_____

My favorite funny competitors in this race:

_____

Trickiest puzzle: _____

_____

Bonus points I earned: _____

And the Ohio winners are:

_____

I visited Oklahoma. ☐ I want to visit. ☐

People I know: _____

_____

My favorite places to visit: _____

_____

One amazing fact I didn't know: _____

_____

My favorite funny competitors in this race:

_____

Trickiest puzzle: _____

_____

Bonus points I earned: _____

And the Oklahoma winners are:

_____

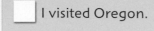 I visited Oregon.   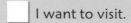 I want to visit.

People I know: _____

_____

My favorite places to visit: _____

_____

One amazing fact I didn't know: _____

_____

My favorite funny competitors in this race:

_____

Trickiest puzzle: _____

_____

Bonus points I earned: _____

And the Oregon winners are:

_____

☐ I visited Pennsylvania.　☐ I want to visit.

People I know: _____

_____

My favorite places to visit: _____ ___

_____

One amazing fact I didn't know: _____

_____

My favorite funny competitors in this race:

_____

Trickiest puzzle: _____

_____

Bonus points I earned: _____

And the Pennsylvania winners are:

_____

49

☐ I visited Rhode Island. ☐ I want to visit.

People I know: _____

_____

My favorite places to visit: _____

_____

One amazing fact I didn't know: _____

_____

My favorite funny competitors in this race:

_____

Trickiest puzzle: _____

_____

Bonus points I earned: _____

And the Rhode Island winners are:

_____

☐ I visited South Carolina.   ☐ I want to visit.

People I know: _____

_____

My favorite places to visit: _____

_____

One amazing fact I didn't know: _____

_____

My favorite funny competitors in this race:

_____

Trickiest puzzle: _____

_____

Bonus points I earned: _____

And the South Carolina winners are:

_____

☐ I visited South Dakota. ☐ I want to visit.

People I know: _____

_____

My favorite places to visit: _____

_____

One amazing fact I didn't know: _____

_____

My favorite funny competitors in this race:

_____

Trickiest puzzle: _____

_____

Bonus points I earned: _____

And the South Dakota winners are:

_____

I visited Tennessee. I want to visit.

People I know: _____

_____

My favorite places to visit: _____

_____

One amazing fact I didn't know: _____

_____

My favorite funny competitors in this race: _____

_____

Trickiest puzzle: _____

_____

Bonus points I earned: _____

And the Tennessee winners are:

_____

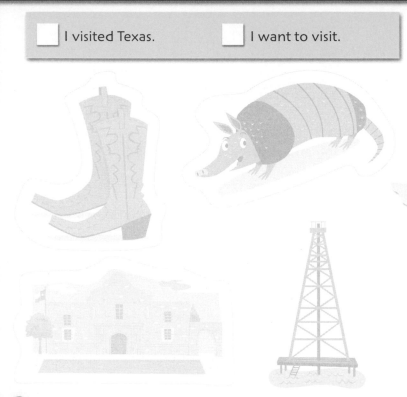

☐ I visited Texas.   ☐ I want to visit.

People I know: _____

_____

My favorite places to visit: _____

_____

One amazing fact I didn't know: _____

_____

My favorite funny competitors in this race:

_____

Trickiest puzzle: _____

_____

Bonus points I earned: _____

And the Texas winners are:

_____

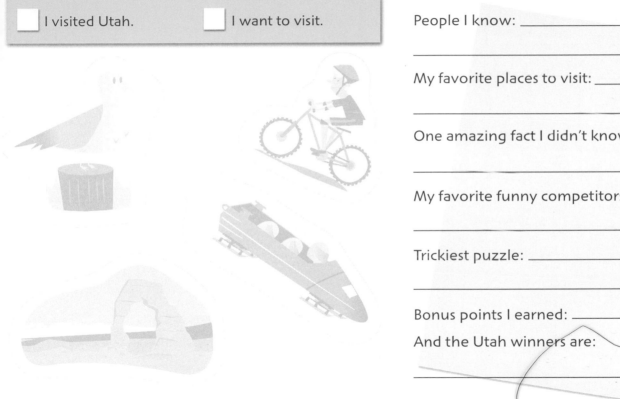

I visited Utah.   I want to visit.

People I know: _____

_____

My favorite places to visit: _____

_____

One amazing fact I didn't know: _____

_____

My favorite funny competitors in this race:

_____

Trickiest puzzle: _____

_____

Bonus points I earned: _____

And the Utah winners are:

_____

☐ I visited Vermont.   ☐ I want to visit.

People I know: _____

_____

My favorite places to visit: _____

_____

One amazing fact I didn't know: _____

_____

My favorite funny competitors in this race:

_____

Trickiest puzzle: _____

_____

Bonus points I earned: _____

And the Vermont winners are:

_____

[ ] I visited Virginia.   [ ] I want to visit.

People I know: _____

_____

My favorite places to visit: _____

_____

One amazing fact I didn't know: _____

_____

My favorite funny competitors in this race: _____

_____

Trickiest puzzle: _____

_____

Bonus points I earned: _____

And the Virginia winners are:

_____

☐ I visited Washington.   ☐ I want to visit.

People I know: _____

_____

My favorite places to visit: _____

_____

One amazing fact I didn't know: _____

_____

My favorite funny competitors in this race:

_____

Trickiest puzzle: _____

_____

Bonus points I earned: _____

And the Washington winners are:

_____

WEST VIRGINIA

The Mountain State   35th State

☐ I visited West Virginia.   ☐ I want to visit.

People I know: _____

_____

My favorite places to visit: _____

_____

One amazing fact I didn't know: _____

_____

My favorite funny competitors in this race:

_____

Trickiest puzzle: _____

_____

Bonus points I earned: _____

And the West Virginia winners are:

_____

59

☐ I visited Wisconsin. ☐ I want to visit.

People I know: _____

_____

My favorite places to visit: _____

_____

One amazing fact I didn't know: _____

_____

My favorite funny competitors in this race:

_____

Trickiest puzzle: _____

_____

Bonus points I earned: _____

And the Wisconsin winners are:

_____

☐ I visited Wyoming.   ☐ I want to visit.

People I know: _____

_____

My favorite places to visit: _____

_____

One amazing fact I didn't know: _____

_____

My favorite funny competitors in this race:

_____

Trickiest puzzle: _____

_____

Bonus points I earned: _____

And the Wyoming winners are:

_____

Travel Notes

Travel Notes

The Big Finish

Congratulations! You have finished your **Which Way USA** race across America. Tripp and Scout crossed the finish line in every state. You helped them win as many races as possible, and you learned a lot about the USA, too! Now you have one last chance to write about what you liked best.

The number of races that Tripp, Scout, and I won: _____

The state in which I scored the most bonus points: _____

The state race I liked best:

_____

The kind of puzzle I liked best:

_____

My favorite race teams were:

Aretha Flowers and Beau Kay
☐

Huck Hyuck and Lotta Laughs
☐

Laverne and Burly
☐

Boris and Ivana Wynn
☐

Clueless and Lark
☐

Rabbit and Cadabra
☐

Bubba Gum and Pops
☐

Flora and Fawn
☐

Hyde and Zeke
☐

Charley and Rhoda Horse
☐

Kent Stop and Stu Late
☐

Topsy and Turvy
☐

Eb and Flo
☐

Penn and Speller
☐

Ruff and Rocky Rhodes
☐

Kareem Cheese and Shelly
☐

Mel Box and Fred Ex
☐

Zig and Zag
☐

If I could visit just one place in the USA it would be:

_____

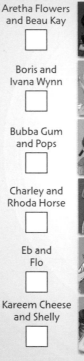
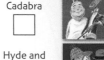

64